Short Course Workbook

Bryan Coombs

Pitman

PITMAN PUBLISHING LIMITED
128 Long Acre, London WC2E 9AN

A Longman Group Company

© Pitman Publishing Ltd 1986

First published in Great Britain 1986

British Library Cataloguing in Publication Data
Coombs, Bryan
  Pitman 2000 shorthand short course workbook.
  1. Shorthand—Pitman—Examinations, questions, etc.
  I. Title
  653'.4242'076   Z56.2.PS

Text set in 10/12 pt Univers Light
Printed and bound in Great Britain
at The Bath Press, Avon

ISBN 0 273 02325 X

to criticism from the leadership of the opposition and is an acknowledgement of the need for an urgent adjustment to existing schemes. The appointment of a new Minister for the Environment on 23rd May, with an additional budget of £50,000,000, is a further acknowledgement of the need for a totally new approach to the problems.

Blank line drill

1   The gross profit of £1,560,000 was a disappointment and share prices reacted quickly.
2   After several postponements the meeting started at 1500 hours under a new chairmanship.
3   Actually no more than eight or nine attended out of a membership of over 200.
4   Certainly some amendments are urgently needed and an announcement will be made on 22nd July.
5   Eventually the meeting ended at 5 o'clock and apparently there had been some lively discussion.

Dictation

Dear Householder
On 7th April I took over the ownership of your local General Store and you may have seen the announcement in the Daily News. The store will be open from 0800 to 2000 hours Monday to Saturday and eventually will trade seven days a week. Basically we can supply most small household items and a wide assortment of fresh and frozen foods, all realistically priced. I certainly believe you will be pleasantly surprised at the improvements introduced and I will happily arrange for home deliveries. Shopping locally does make sense and I look forward to welcoming you to General Store very soon. Yours sincerely, Richard Smith, Proprietor

Contents

Introductory note

The material in this book has to be used in conjunction with *Short Course*. After completing a unit of *Short Course*, say Unit 1, then turn to Unit 1 of *Workbook* and use the additional practice material. As soon as this has been done proceed to Unit 2 of *Short Course*.

Each exercise in Unit 1 of *Workbook* is accompanied by suggestions on how best to use the material and these study plans can be used throughout the book, or adapted to individual needs. It is important to take the continuous material from dictation, live or recorded.

Unit 15

Short form and phrase drill

Your attention is called to the large amount of information available on both sides of the Atlantic Ocean about qualifications which have international recognition. The Medical Association has such information for both doctors and nurses, much to the satisfaction of members. This exchange of information within the professions is very useful.

Blank line drill

1 Exceptional values in stationery are mentioned in the publication from International Papers Limited.
2 Instructions about production modifications to the television sets we sell have been received.
3 Discussions took place about the position of the organisation at national and international level.
4 Attention is called to the decision that all requisitions within the section be retained for taxation purposes.
5 Additional information is necessary and an explanation for the cancellation of the order.

Dictation

Memo

To: All Directors   **From**: Managing Director
Subject: Expansion Overseas

A decision must be taken immediately about expansion and the setting up of international subsidiaries. The information we have suggests that the additional capital required will be available and applications for grants will be successful. Inflation in some areas under consideration is exceptionally high and special attention must be paid to this. Great satisfaction can be derived from the fact that we are in such a sound financial position but action on the new proposals cannot be delayed.

Unit 16

Short form and phrase drill

The government announcement about new enterprise zones is in need of enlargement to become totally clear. Apparently this is in response

Unit 1

Short form drill

It is essential to know each short form and be able to write all of them without hesitancy. Drilling short forms individually and in groups will help to master these outlines. Always say the word to yourself as you write the outline; this is your own personal dictation system.

Write along the line, horizontally, to drill an individual outline → and down the page, vertically, to drill the group of outlines ↓ . If, when the lines are full, you still feel unsure about some outlines, continue drilling by writing over the top of your outlines.

put

be

to

too/two

of

and

do

it

the

a/an

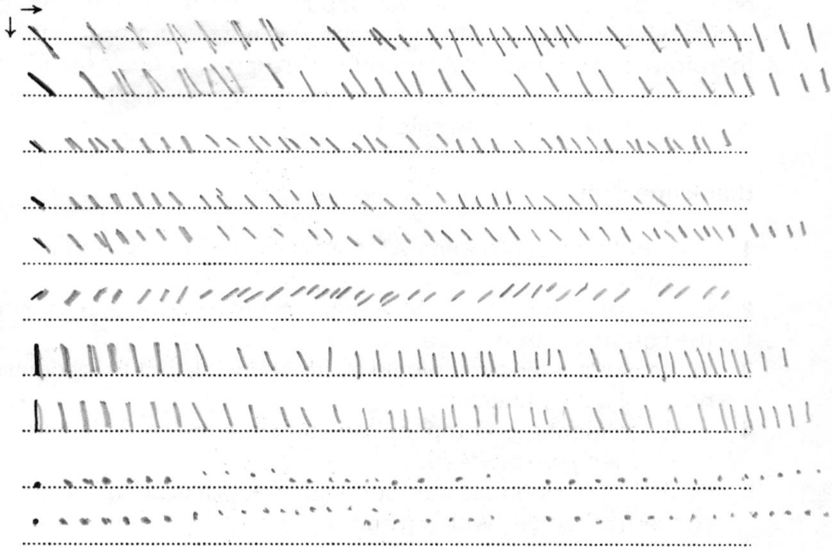

Short form and phrase drill

The material which follows contains all the short forms just drilled, and many phrases. This material is very easy and should be read, drilled and written rapidly.

1 Read through the sentences as quickly as you can. Repeat the reading until you can read each outline without any hesitation.
2 Copy the exercise, writing quickly and accurately.

which I supported, you are the most experienced in handling tenders and dealing with printers and other suppliers. The materials you order will be for the whole group with expenditure amounting to many thousands of pounds and will include office furniture. I know you will make a first class job of it. If there is any way I can be of assistance call in at my office any afternoon.

Unit 14

Short form and phrase drill

Anybody who pays income tax recognises it is essential to do so but this does little or nothing to take away the pain. Without such a tax nothing could be done in the way of public services and those in control would be without any form of finance. It is not uncommon to find therefore that the majority of people who earn money do in fact pay income tax. Anyhow, whoever is in charge of financing the country will continue to tax wages and salaries.

Blank line drill

1 The company conference will concern itself with the innumerable tax controls.
2 It is illegal to import certain goods without a permit and unfortunately the controls will continue.
3 In the circumstances it would be irresponsible not to recognise the need for safety checks.
4 I am confident this company can complete the contract and recommend we proceed.
5 Having a considerable number of contracts it is unnecessary to concern ourselves with any more.

Dictation

Dear Mr Jones
Thank you for returning the completed contract so promptly. I am confident that work on the new factory can begin without any unnecessary delay. All concerned with this project recognise how urgent it is to complete on schedule. It would be irresponsible of me to say nothing can go wrong because unfortunately unexpected events occur and of course we cannot control the weather. However I do believe we can fulfil our contract. Yours sincerely, David Harvey, Contracts Manager

3 Take from dictation at least three times. After each dictation rapid–read the material. Increase the speed of the third dictation.

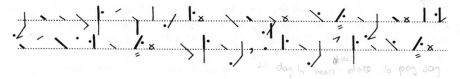

Blank line drill

1 Read through the material as quickly as you can before attempting to take it from dictation. Check the Key if any outline causes hesitation.

2 Complete the blank lines from dictation.

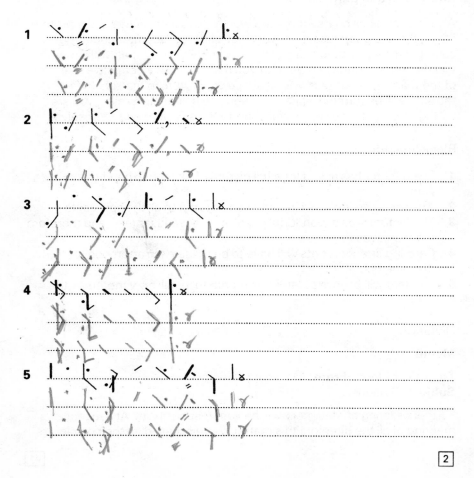

Dictation

Dear Mrs Smith
From time to time we have quantities of stock on sale at bargain prices
in order to move the stock quickly. This month we are having what we
believe to be our best sale of quality goods to equip a kitchen; prices
are the lowest for years. When the sale opens there will be a rush. You
will not need to wait until then because all of our regular customers may
attend next week. You may purchase immediately or request items to
be reserved for you. Why not come and see for yourself; you will not
be disappointed. Yours sincerely, Sales Manager

Unit 13

Short form and phrase drill

After a secretarial course there are wonderful opportunities and therefore
I think there is good reason to work just a little harder throughout the
course. Further training takes place at work where the staff will show
you the office routine in order that you may become an effective member
of the team. Your attitude will influence your future in that job. In fact
the staff will be forming a picture of you and if, in their opinion, you are
willing to learn, those wonderful opportunities will present themselves.

Blank line drill

1   The director has asked for a full picture of heating expenditure this
    winter.
2   After an interview it is kinder to send a letter to all the applicants.
3   The lecture was a wonderful mixture of fact and fantasy, and therefore
    most enjoyable.
4   Catering arrangements will have to be made each afternoon for the
    machine operators.
5   Tenders will be invited later this month to install new meters at the
    centre.

Dictation

Memo

To: Senior Clerk   **From**: Managing Director
Subject: Stationery

Further ordering of stationery will be your responsibility. At a recent
meeting of all the directors this matter was discussed. In their opinion,

Dictation

1   Read through the sentences and use a pencil to encircle any outline you cannot read.
2   Refer to the Key at the back of the book and check those encircled outlines.
3   Drill the outlines which caused a problem. This drilling must be thorough enough so that you will never again hesitate over any of these outlines.
4   Repeat the reading several times until you can read the sentences as quickly as if they were typescript.
5   Take the material from dictation. Read back your notes. Check outlines. Drill corrections. Repeat the dictation at least three times. There must always be some drilling of corrections or rapid–reading of the material, or both, in between each dictation.

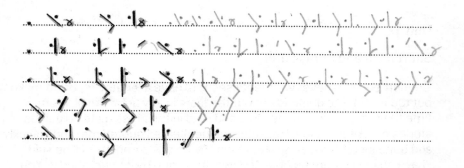

Unit 2

Short form drill

today	
large	
which	
to be	
had/dollar	

3

Dictation

Memo

To: Factory Manager   **From**: Sales Manager
Subject: Exports

I expect demand for our goods to break all records this month. In order to meet these demands, particularly exports, I need your support. It is a pity this is such short notice, and I regret it, but it cannot be helped. Please arrange two late night shifts to start immediately. Standard overtime rates will be paid. Please let me have details of any arrangements you make, and let me hear from you if you have any particular problems.

Unit 12

Short form and phrase drill

Gentlemen, Whenever we meet I seem to have a lengthy report to make but today I am not going to set out the facts in any great detail. From time to time we hear on the radio and read in the press quite ridiculous stories of takeover bids. Recently one gentleman quoted me, and I quickly add quite incorrectly, as saying when I retire this company will be sold. I have no idea where he obtained this story, or why he published it. You will not be surprised to hear, Gentlemen, our trade is booming and towards the end of the month you will see that our trade figures are quite the best we have ever had.

Blank line drill

1 When qualified in a foreign language you are better equipped to learn shorthand quickly.
2 Request help whenever you are about to use a machine for the first time.
3 I do not know why, but your sales area has quite the lowest figures on record.
4 At some time we shall want a quick quote from you for white bond typing paper.
5 We are required to create equal opportunities, not only in offices but wherever vacancies occur.

Short form and phrase drill

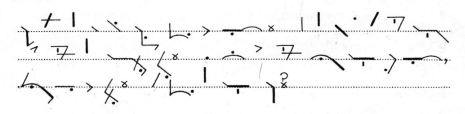

Blank line drill

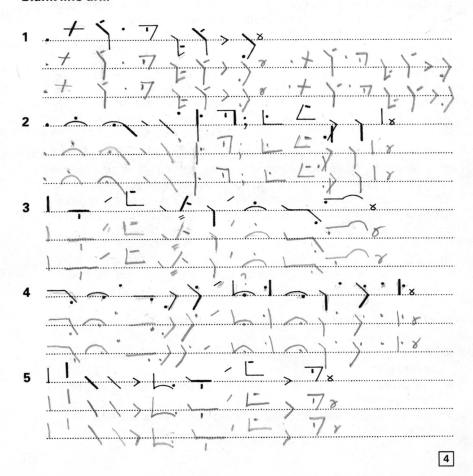

4

3 From a general analysis of the annual sales in the United States we still lead our rivals.

4 We supply all the leading labels and I am enclosing samples for your approval.

5 Rightly or wrongly April is still the beginning of the financial year for us.

Dictation

Dear Mr Lowe

I am sorry to learn of the problems you are having with the oil burning cooker we supplied last April. I am thankful to you for giving such a full analysis of the troubles which will also prove invaluable to our service people. I can assure you this company will fulfil the terms of the guarantee. Our service people will call this week and you will be advised of the time by telephone. Please allow plenty of time for the cooker to cool before the visit to enable a full check to be carried out. Yours sincerely, Manager

Unit 11

Short form and phrase drill

According to the experts your shorthand skill develops immediately if you practise daily. You are able to see progress, particularly in your reading and writing speeds, that you could not see before. Accordingly I think it is necessary to take immediate steps to start daily practice in order to ensure progress. I hope you will be able to do so immediately; you cannot afford to delay.

Blank line drill

1 Minutes of the meeting were recorded and details will be given in the report.

2 Doubts about the methods used were expressed but I doubt they will affect results.

3 We have made solid progress and have high hopes for both home and export sales.

4 The attitude of the salesman irritated customers and he was sent here for training.

5 Do we need to spend hundreds of thousands of pounds on advertising?

Dictation

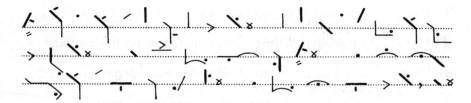

Unit 3

Short form drill

all

together

altogether

as/has

Mrs

is/his

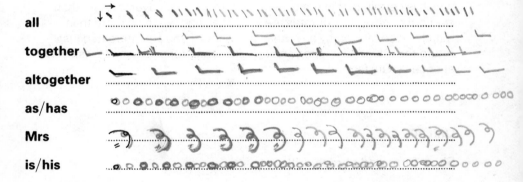

Short form and phrase drill

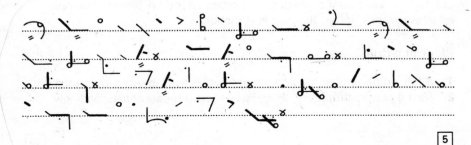

5

Blank line drill

1 Property owners never have enough insurance and it is necessary to inform them.
2 Many of the managers in the country require training and this must be done at once.
3 Several inquiries have been received on the answering machine and it has been worth the expense.
4 A bonus is often paid to a number of the men and women but it is never enough.
5 Arrange the staff party and announce it via the notice board within the next few days.

Dictation

Dear Sir

I am writing to inform you of our new car insurance scheme which is better than anything we have offered before. We have been in the insurance business for many years and now we have designed a scheme which is certain to win many new customers. The cover is larger than ever but once again our rates are very keen and we think more than match those offered by any other company. If you are interested just return the attached coupon and I shall arrange for someone to visit you at once. Yours faithfully

Unit 10

Short form and phrase drill

I am thankful this new plan will also be influential in enlarging our business. I acknowledge this is largely due to your specialist subject knowledge. You took it upon yourself to develop this policy and I believe it will be the main reason for the success of the General Oil Company Limited. As soon as we can obtain approval of the full Board it will only be a few weeks before the plan is launched.

Blank line drill

1 A full length film on the subject of travel is available at a low rental.
2 All the people employed there have regular meals at a surprisingly low cost.

Blank line drill

1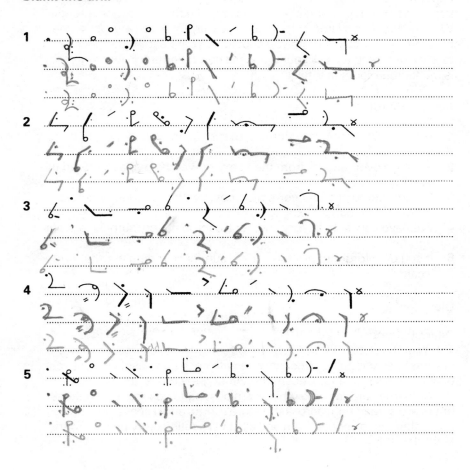

2

3

4

5

Dictation

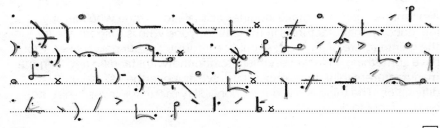

6

Paper Makers in December. The major commercial firms are very much larger today and of course their aim is to make more and more profits. Working for such a large corporation you may think you are just a statistic but from your first day there you should try your best. Remember to take extra care, check all your work and correct errors. Your progress is measured. Yours faithfully

Blank line drill

1 Advertisers try to put extreme pressure on their readers with free offers.
2 Shall we ever recover from the summer weather we all suffered this year?
3 Remember to put your correct address, with post code, otherwise there may be difficulties.
4 We have very satisfactory and, for December, very surprising profit figures.
5 If you ever forget to pay the agreed sum each month we shall write a card.

Dictation

Dear Customer
This month for the first time we are offering free of charge a birthday or Christmas wrapping paper service with each purchase. I must stress of course this is just for December. Other great offers are described in the Christmas programme which I am posting to you today, and these offers are spread right across the store. Come and discover just how much there is to choose from and all at very satisfactory prices. Yours faithfully

Unit 9

Short form and phrase drill

Next month, January, make inquiries and talk to anyone who has any influence on manufacturers in this city. Anyone who is responsible for the manufacture of anything should be informed of our newspaper. We have something, in fact everything, to offer notwithstanding anything the manufacturers think they know of us. We do nevertheless have difficulties. The thing is it is our responsibility more than ever to get the correct facts to them.

Unit 4

Short form drill

almost

first

who

but

owe/oh

on

Short form and phrase drill

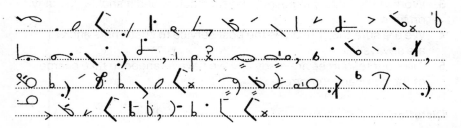

Blank line drill

1

2

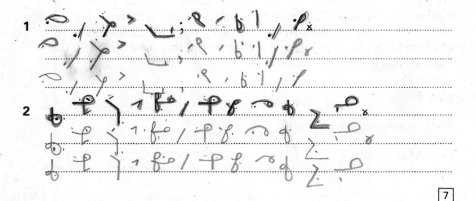

7

to a task you think is difficult. This form of studying does make for success. You have to have both faith and positive thinking.

Unit 7

Short form and phrase drill

We are sure your air bookings are satisfactory for your visit tomorrow but we shall check the hour you should be arriving. We have already arranged for a car. I am sorry your stay with us this year is just for a few days. You may be required to visit the factory during your visit. If you require to see the work being carried out just say so and I shall make arrangements.

Blank line drill

1 They are to receive the receipts by tomorrow, Thursday, which is satisfactory.
2 The purpose of this exercise on words is to remedy errors and aid reading and writing.
3 Work at the factory appears to be satisfactory and it should be ready on time.
4 We are sure this firm gives the best service to customers and we are always fair.
5 All of our resources are ready and we have arranged to take charge of the company tomorrow.

Dictation

We have arranged a party on Thursday to mark the success of the firm this year, so check your diary. We have reserved two large rooms to cope with all the guests, both office and factory staff and some of our customers. Mr Roger Moore, who is on our Board, is to make a few remarks and refer to the shares scheme for the staff. During his term of office Mr Moore has had to work fast to get this scheme ready. We are sure this is the right road to take.

Unit 8

Short form and phrase drill

Dear Miss Fraser
Just a few words of advice before you take up your post at Commercial

3

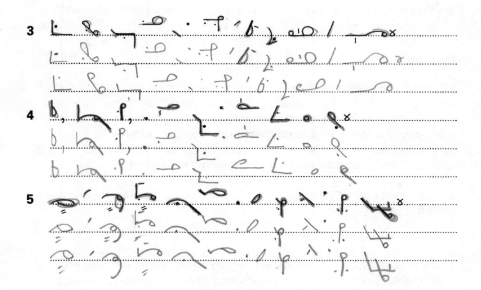

4

5

Dictation

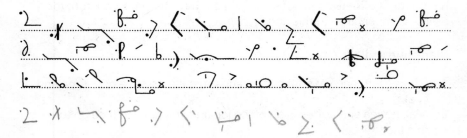

5 This month we shall get out and occupy a choice site on the south side of this city.

Dictation

We shall see them all and the aim is to sway them on the issue of duties as set out at the talks on Tuesday. It was decided this month is the best time to discuss both duties and wages. This is due to the switches we wish to make. We assume most of them do wish to assist and it is suggested we discuss wages first. We must show the team the choices and ask them to take time and to choose which way to go.

Unit 6

Short form and phrase drill

Thank you so much for the cheque, which is the largest we have had. The chief difficulty we have to face is how to say thank you to all who have posted cheques. We have office staff but it is difficult for them to cope. We shall have to have several forms for them to use, which would be the most effective way of saving time. I have to thank you, too, for giving so much time to this activity.

Blank line drill

1 Office staff face vast difficulties and must aim to save both time and costs.
2 Making tea and coffee is an office job and you have to face up to this fact.
3 A vote would divide the office staff, five saying yes and six defeating it.
4 Put the shop takings in the safe and if you have to go out of the city give me the key.
5 We have to face the facts and we must be both tough and effective.

Dictation

I wish to give you some advice on the most effective way to study. You have to give up so much time each day and devote it to studying. How you study is a big issue. Most of us achieve success if we divide the time we have. We should give as much time to an activity so as to be effective. Give so much time to a task which you think is easy and move

Unit 5

Short form drill

we

yesterday

although

always

shall

should

think

this

ought

Short form and phrase drill

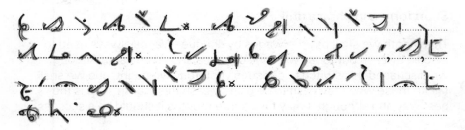

Blank line drill

1

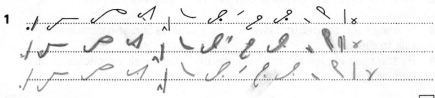

9

who is a boss of a large department, supposes it is easy and suggests it has to be the first job. Mrs Best says the success of each department owes much to easy access to the post but the job does test, so it is a top job.

Blank line drill

1 Master each passage of the book; stop and test at each stage.
2 Diseases exhaust the body and the statistics which exist suggest mass tests to check causes.
3 Take steps to get access to a cassette and just see the success which comes.
4 At first, it must be said, the cost to take a stock check is steep.
5 Mr and Mrs Thomas may be almost the first to set up a city book business.

Dictation

Ask each department to keep statistics of each job because it pays to check job costs. Such statistics assist to keep costs steady and it is easy to make such a check. Most departments discuss costs and take steps to stop mistakes. Much of the success is because of the easy access to costs.

Unit 5

Short form and phrase drill

This month we shall pay the wages by cheque. Wages always used to be paid by cash but today we think cheques should be used. Although we discussed this switch to cheques yesterday we ought, and we shall, talk to those who may wish to be paid by cash this month. This is the best way and although it may take some months it should be a success.

Blank line drill

1 Each week we must watch out for waste and use ways to stop it.
2 Yes, switch to cassettes and show them the way they should use them.
3 She showed them but it was a waste of time and she decided to talk to them.
4 By the time we issued these items on Tuesday all the choice shops had bought.

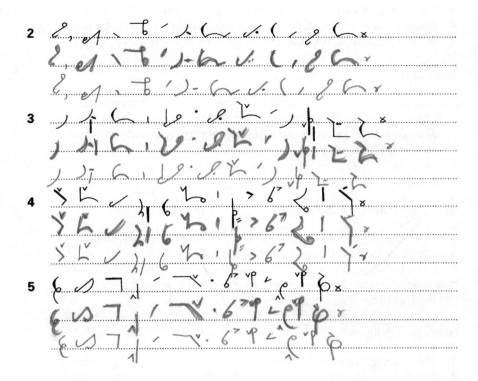

Dictation

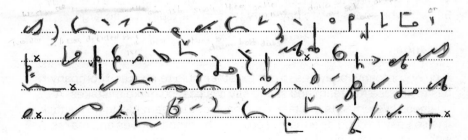

3 Do go and talk to Joe today and aim to keep calm.
4 Keep me a key to each page and it may aid me to do a page a day.
5 It had to be put to the team to go and talk to the coach.

Dictation

Joe bought a boat and had to tow it to the bay. It had to be a large
teak boat to take to the deep bay. Two of the company team came to
aid Joe. The aim may be to keep the boat and go to it each day. The
team may go to the bay, too.

Unit 3

Short form and phrase drill

Mrs Beck has to put all of the sets of discs together. Ask Mrs Beck
to pick discs to take to Joe. Altogether Joe has to get six. Take all of
his discs to his desk today. Catch Joe at his desk. The disc business
is large and it is up to us all to get together as a team and catch all
the big business.

Blank line drill

1 The system is as easy as it is said to be and it is so cheap to get.
2 Check the jets and set the space of each jet to make the gas escape.
3 Choose a big case which has a zip and which is easy to empty.
4 Ask Mrs Page to add together all the cheques and to see me today.
5 A city business has to pay a city tax and it is a pity it is so large.

Dictation

A busy company today has to get together a big team. Each company
has to choose the team and sad to say it is easy to make mistakes. A
business system sets the tasks and each of the team has to do his task.
It is so easy to cope as a team. Today each company goes and makes
a check to see which of the team sit all day and doze.

Unit 4

Short form and phrase drill

Almost the first job each day is to check the post and put it on the desk
of the boss. At first it may seem to be an easy task, but is it? Mr Stokes,

Unit 6

Short form drill

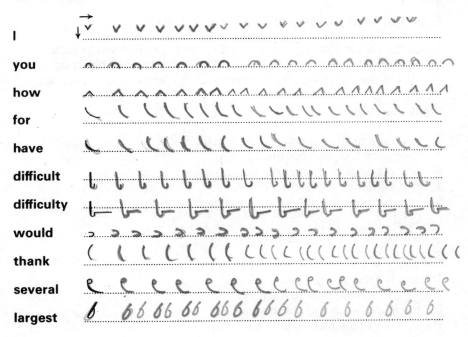

I	
you	
how	
for	
have	
difficult	
difficulty	
would	
thank	
several	
largest	

Short form and phrase drill

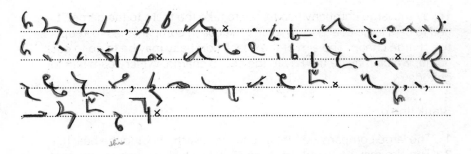

Key

Unit 1

Short form and phrase drill

Teach the two to put the date and to do it each day. Put two to each department. Pay Jay to teach the two. Do aid the two and be an aid to Jay. Put the date to teach, the day to teach and the date to pay Jay.

Blank line drill

1 Pay Jay and eat a cheap peach each day.
2 Date each tape and put the age, too.
3 Teach a page each day and tape it.
4 Pay the department to aid the two to put the date.
5 Do a tape of each department and pay Joe to do it.

Dictation

The pay. Pay the aid.
The aid. Aid the day and pay.
The tape. Tape the date to the page.
Put the age of each and put the date.
The ape ate a peach and a date each day.

Unit 2

Short form and phrase drill

Today the large company had to pay to take the team to the game. It had to be a large coach to cope and the coach company had to keep the charge cheap. The aim of the coach company may be to go to each game, which may be the key to the cheap charge. Which team had to go today?

Blank line drill

1 The large company bought a coach to tow the boat to the beach.
2 The aim may be to put a date code; take chalk to each department to do it.

Blank line drill

1

2

3

4

5

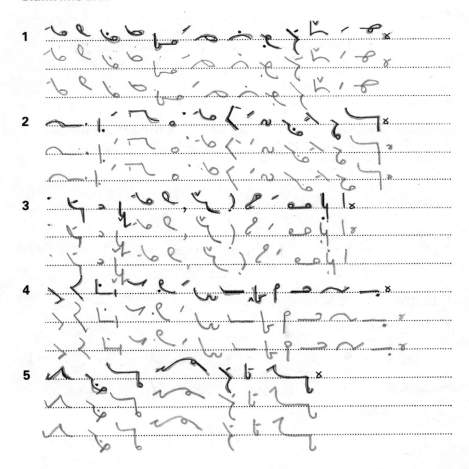

Dictation

4

5

Dictation

29/1

Unit 7

Short form drill

are	
hour/our	
satisfactory	
your	
tomorrow	
year	
with	

Short form and phrase drill

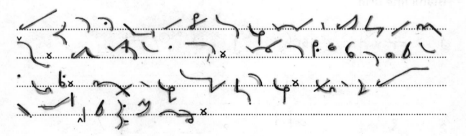

Blank line drill

1

Unit 16

Short form drill

acknowledgement

enlargement

Short form and phrase drill

Homework
27/1

Blank line drill

29/1

1

2

3

2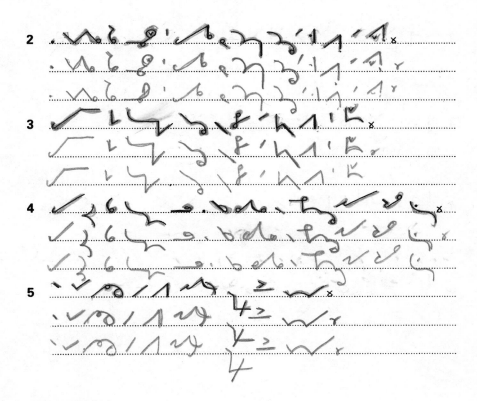

3

4

5

Dictation

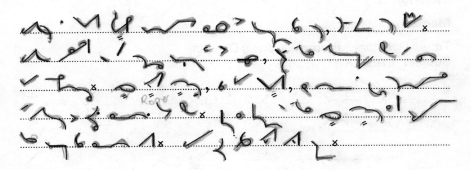

14

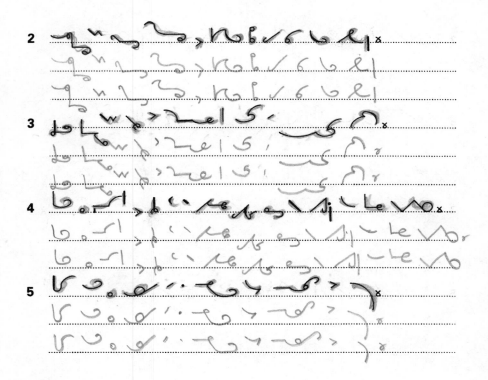

2

3

4

5

Dictation

Memo

To: All Directors   **From**: Managing Director
Subject: Expansion Overseas

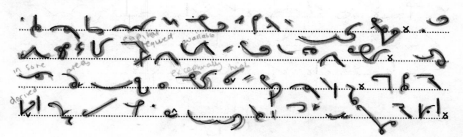

Unit 8

Short form drill

dear

from

before

more

their/there

commercial/
   commercially
very

large

Short form and phrase drill

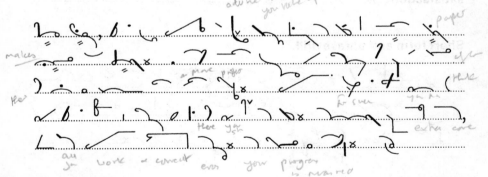

Blank line drill

1

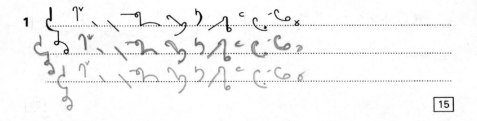

15

Dictation

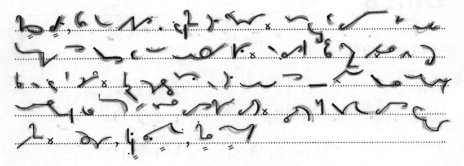

Unit 15

Short form drill

information

satisfaction

Short form and phrase drill

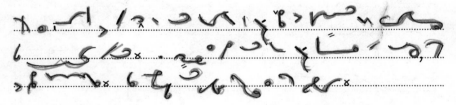

Blank line drill

1

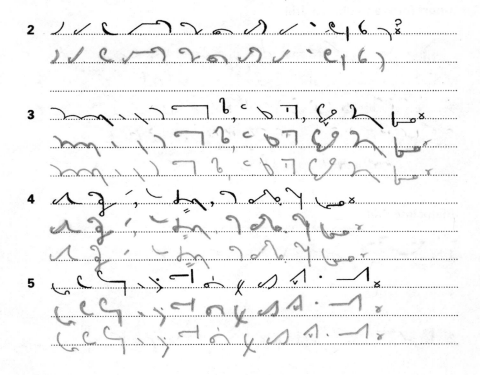

Dictation

Dear customer, this month for the 1st time we are offering free of charge a birthday or Xmas wrapping paper service with each purchase. I must stress of course this is just for December. Other great offers are described in the Xmas programme which I am posting to you today; and these offers are spread right across the store. Come and discover just how much there is to choose from and all at very satisfactory prices – YF

Short form and phrase drill

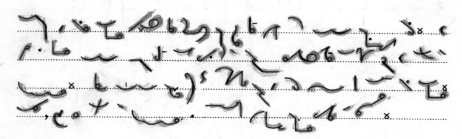

Blank line drill

1.

2.

3.

4.

5.

Unit 9

Short form drill

in/any

influence

January

thing

something

anything

manufacture

manufacturer

anyone

nevertheless

notwithstanding

responsible/
responsibility

Short form and phrase drill

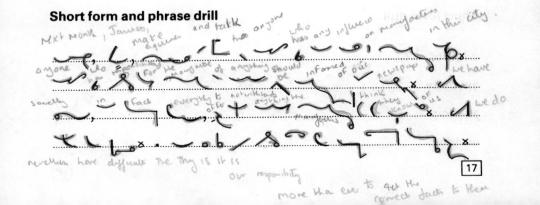

4

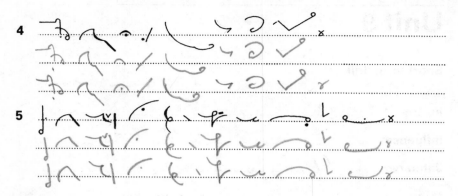

5

Dictation

Memo

To: Senior Clerk   **From**: Managing Director
Subject: Stationery

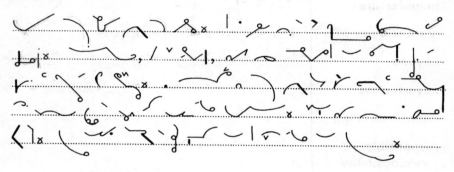

Unit 14

Short form drill

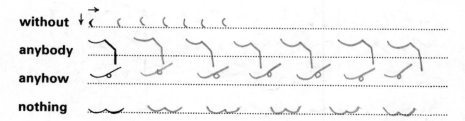

without

anybody

anyhow

nothing

Blank line drill

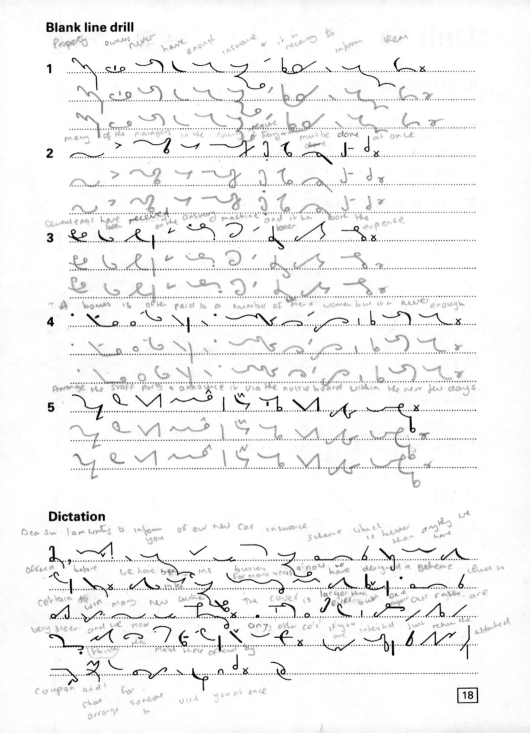

Property owners never have enough insurance & it is necessary to inform them

1

many of the managers in the country of _____ must be done at once

2

several rings have received _____ on the answering machine and it has _____ the expense

3

A bonus is often paid to a number of men & women but it is _____ enough

4

Arrange the staff party & announce it via the notice board within the next few days.

5

Dictation

Dear Sir I am writing to inform you of our new car insurance scheme which is better anything we have offered before we have been ins busin a now we have designed a scheme which is for many years certain to win many new custom The cover is larger than we better but one again our rates are very keen and we now _____ any other co's if you are interested just return the coupon and I _____ Mark those offered by attached for shall someone will you at once arrange to

Unit 13

Short form drill

therefore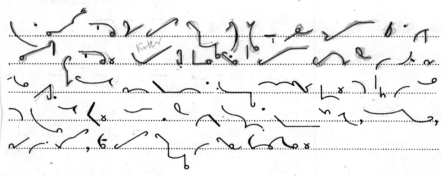

wonderful/
   wonderfully

Short form and phrase drill

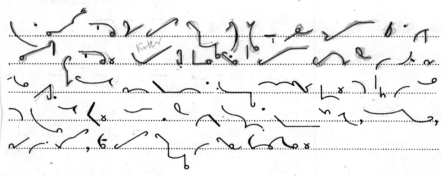

Blank line drill

1

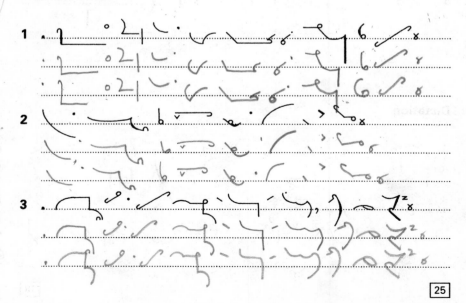

2

3

25

Unit 10

Short form drill

also

will

influential

thankful

enlarge

knowledge

acknowledge

largely

yourself

subject

Short form and phrase drill

Blank line drill

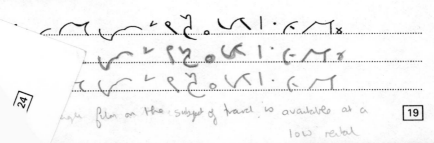

3

4

5

Dictation

2

From a great shopping arena sold in the us we still hold R rivals

3

we supply each label + I am adding samples for your approval

4

Rightly or wrongly April is still the beginning of the financial year for us.

5

Dictation

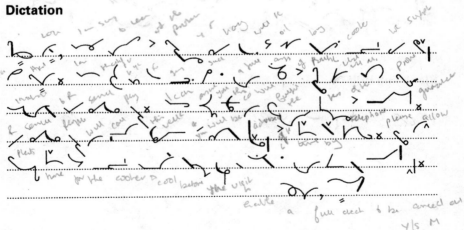

a full elect to be carried out
y/s M

Unit 12

Short form drill

trade/toward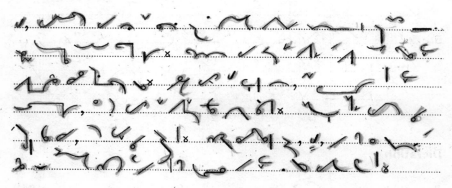

gentleman

gentlemen

Short form and phrase drill

Blank line drill

1

2

Unit 11

Short form drill

immediate

immediately

could

that

able to

cannot

particular

particularly

accord/according/
   according to
   accordingly

Short form and phrase drill

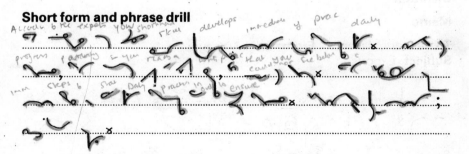

Blank line drill

1

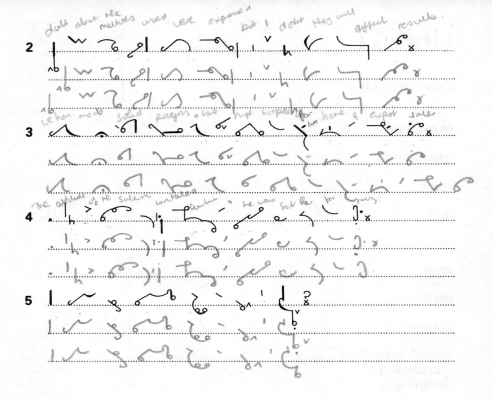

2 ... doubt about the methods used we expressed but I doubt they will affect results.

3 ... we have made solid progress in two high prospect for home & export sales

4 ... the approval of the sales ... in ... we was sell her ...

5 ...

Dictation

Memo

To: Factory Manager   **From**: Sales Manager
Subject: Exports

I expect demand for our goods break all records this Math ...
... share ...